The Odd Squad

HOT CROSS PUNS

by Allan Plenderleith

RAVETTE PUBLISHING

For Laura

The Odd Squad and all related characters © 2009
Created by Allan Plenderleith
www.allanplenderleith.com

First published in 2009 by
Ravette Publishing Limited

ISBN: 978-1-84161-323-9

May the farts be with you...always.

When the boss walked in, Maude was
backing up her stuff on a floppy.

Jeff goes to a bad singles party.

The banana Jeff bought last week
had turned bad.

Randy Maude had actually asked Jeff to put some Barry White on the stereo.

Dug assured the barman,
it was just the beer talking.

Maude's friend was a big slapper.

When Jeff returned to his car, there
was a big bird dropping on it.

This wasn't the blu-ray disc
Jeff thought he had ordered.

Apart from her fit boyfriend, everyone in the nightclub was 'butters'.

When he has a pub lunch, Jeff always orders the chicken in a basque.

The thing Jeff loved most about flying was the complimentary nuts.

Jeff receives a large Czech in the post.

Jeff was worried – Billy seemed to be spending an awful lot of time in *da hood*.

Jeff discovers some dangerous
cookies on his computer.

Jeff's New Year resolution was
to lay off the fags.

Jeff got a deep fat friar for his birthday.

At the club, Maude gets into a
fight with a dirty hoe.

Jeff makes a cat flap.

Jeff is caught smuggling
some dope through customs.

The morning after, Jeff wakes up with a disgusting film on his teeth.

Jeff finds out why the blonde nurse
had a red felt pen.

The doctor told me
to draw blood!

Although the survivors had no food and were miles from anywhere – they needn't worry, because Jeff had remembered the flares.

Suddenly Jeff realises his flies were down.

Dug was surprised to find out his Indian takeaway came with a free nan.

Dug was really into *gangsta wrap*.

Finally Maude finds an
easy way to get thinner.

Unfortunately, during his golf game, Jeff's ball landed in a bit of rough.

Patsy's man was a grate kisser.

Jeff likes to hang out with his mates down the pub.

Jeff had an annoying hare in his mouth.

For his birthday, Billy had asked
for an Iron Man costume.

Maude was suffering from
irritable bowl syndrome.

Maude was horrified to discover Jeff's jazz mags under the bed.

Jeff spends another weekend
getting lashed.

Maude walked into the bathroom to find Jeff playing with himself.

Jeff finally found a job where he was out standing in his field.

Once again, Jeff was overdrawn.

Maude really loved her new jogging bottoms.

As he got older, Alf began having
trouble with his joints.

Whilst out boozing, Dug and his mates put their money in the kitty.

Unfortunately, every time Jeff opens the front door, the dog makes a bolt for it.

Dug takes his mates out to get mashed up.

Jeff had a feeling his birthday parcel came from Amazon.

Jeff had his mother's nose.

Jeff regretted asking the barber
for a 'number two'.

Maude looks up an old friend.

For her birthday, Maude's boyfriend gives her multiple organisms.

Once again, the coffee machine was out of order.

Jeff watches a new TV programme which was paper view.

Billy impresses the girls with his
very own poo bear.

Jeff arrived for their date, but unfortunately Maude had just popped out.

Jeff loves potato wedgies.

Maude was finding potty training
very challenging.

When the barman wasn't looking,
Dug pulled a pint.

Half way through wiping his bum,
the toilet paper ran out.

Jeff bought a sat-chav.

Maude had locked her shelf out again.

Once again, Jeff had to work late
because they were short-staffed.

Jeff treats Maude to a slap-up meal.

As Jeff turned on his PC, he realised it had been attacked by spam.

Jeff and Maude visit the
Great Sphincter of Egypt.

The strawberries Maude had got from the market were completely tasteless.

Whilst out fishing, Jeff's boat was pulled out by some strong currants.

On the way to school, Billy gets stung by a bee.

Alf knew to leave Lily alone when she was going through *the change*.

Jeff spent his Saturday watching the big match.

Dug had heard if you don't want to get a girl pregnant, withdraw at the last moment.

Jeff's new computer came with the wrong kind of ram.

Jeff got bluetooth for his birthday.

In his old age, Alf got into crosswords.

Jeff had actually asked for a new cologne for his birthday.

Jeff visits the doctor to have
a worrying mole removed.

Dug couldn't wait to get his date
home to see her giant pussy.